986.3 MAR   12720

Markun, Patricia Maloney
First book of the Panama
Canal.

DATE   BORROWER'S NAME

986.3 MAR   12720   1167

Markun, Patricia Maloney
First book of the Panama
Canal.   nal.

TO DAVE

who, as Lt. David J. Markun, AUS First Mate of the FS 313, USATC, brought us in roundabout fashion to the Panama Canal

THE FIRST BOOK OF THE
PANAMA CANAL

by PATRICIA MALONEY MARKUN

Pictures by LILI RÉTHI

FRANKLIN WATTS
NEW YORK

The author acknowledges thanks for information and assistance to Governor William E. Potter of the Panama Canal Zone; to Mr. William E. Arey, Jr., Public Information Director of the Panama Canal Company, and his assistant, Mrs. Eleanor McIlhenny; to Captain W. S. Rodiman, USN, Marine Director; to Louise Arey for an idea and Peggy Miller for her encouragement; to Louise Escalona for her invaluable assistance. Special thanks go to Captain Jens Nilsen, Panama Canal pilot, whose knowledge and love of the ships of the world brought alive for me the adventure of the Panama Canal.

Contents

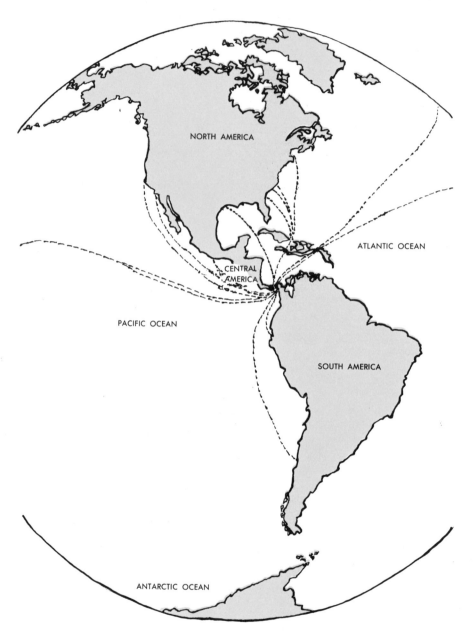

Ship routes from all over the world funnel through the Panama Canal

A Pilot "Puts a Ship Through"

It is five o'clock in the morning in the Panama Canal Zone — and very quiet. Suddenly Captain Jens Nilsen's telephone rings. At once he is awake.

"A chauffeur will call for you in thirty minutes," a voice says, as the captain listens. "You will be taking the Swedish freighter *Tosca* through, northbound as number three transit."

It is the dispatcher from the marine control board in Balboa, Panama Canal Zone, giving the captain his orders for the day. Soon Captain Nilsen will be guiding a ship through the famous fifty-mile-long waterway that connects the Atlantic and Pacific oceans. He is a Panama Canal pilot.

Forty-five minutes later he climbs into a white Panama Canal launch at a little dock outside Balboa Harbor, on the Pacific Ocean. He is wearing a lightweight tropical suit and a pith helmet, for he will spend much of his day in the sun.

Soon the little launch is tossing through rough waters on its way out to where the big ships are anchored. It weaves in and out among them — the Danish *Bella Dan*, the *Hai Siu* from Free China, the British freighters *Dunedin Star* and *Napier Star,* the Liberian *Kaen Naess*, and many others, all waiting to go through the Panama Canal.

At last the launch comes alongside a big gray, white, and yellow freighter, marked *Tosca* in white letters. Sweden's flag flies from her stern. In the faint light of sunrise a blue-and-yellow-striped pennant waves at her mast. In ship's language it means, "We request a pilot."

A rope ladder has been thrown over the side of the *Tosca*. The launch moves over to it carefully. First the pilot's portable

1

A pilot goes out to the waiting ships

two-way radio is hauled aboard on a line. Then Captain Nilsen stands on the edge of the tossing launch, holding the rail for support. The tiny craft rides up and down on the huge waves beside the towering ship.

The launch rises high on a wave crest. One — two — three! Captain Nilsen reaches out and grabs the hanging ladder. He holds on tight with hands and feet, then quickly scrambles upward. Beneath him the launch putt-putts away.

On the *Tosca's* deck a ship's officer is waiting. He leads Captain Nilsen along flight after flight of stairs, high up to the place of command, the bridge of the ship. A tall officer stands there. The four stripes on his sleeve show that he is the captain of the *Tosca.* He greets Captain Nilsen and introduces him to the other officers on the bridge. Then Captain Nilsen takes command, and the *Tosca's* captain moves back on the bridge.

2

A member of the crew has taken down the "request a pilot" flag. In its place he now raises the pennant meaning number three and, beneath it, the half-red, half-white flag that means, "We have a pilot aboard." The number-three flag means that the *Tosca* is to be third in line, going through the canal. The number pennant's position *above* the pilot's flag means that the ship is northbound through the canal to the Atlantic Ocean. When a ship carries the number pennant *below* the pilot's flag, it is going south to the Pacific. Because of the way the narrow land neck of Panama lies, the canal runs nearly north and south.

Now on the forward mast of the *Tosca* the flag of the United States is raised. This is the "courtesy flag." All the ships of the world fly it when they travel through this waterway that was built by the United States.

When the *Tosca* arrived at the canal's entrance late yesterday,

3

she put up the yellow quarantine flag. The Panama Canal's boarding officer made the first trip to the ship. The *Tosca* had passed through the canal many times before, so the boarding officer had a record of her "admeasurement" — that is, her size and the amount of cargo she could carry. With this information the officer could tell how much the ship should pay in tolls for passage through the canal.

The officer checked the kind of cargo aboard. If it had been explosive — munitions, gasoline, or certain chemicals — special safety rules would have been enforced. He also checked to see if there was any illness aboard. If there had been smallpox, cholera, or any of a list of other contagious diseases, the ship would have been quarantined. In that case, she would not have been able to go through the canal for a certain number of days.

But the *Tosca* passed inspection. Quickly the boarding officer added up the tonnage and figured her tolls bill. The agent for the ship's owners had already paid to the Panama Canal treasurer the money to cover the tolls. The ship was cleared, and the yellow quarantine flag was lowered. Then she was free to request a pilot.

Now, the next morning, the pilot checks his watch against the ship's clock, which is ringing four bells. It is 6 A. M. — time for ships to start moving through the Panama Canal.

"Slow speed ahead!" the pilot orders.

"Slow speed ahead!" the quartermaster repeats. The *Tosca* makes ready to enter the canal.

No ship goes through the Panama Canal unaided. "Putting through a ship" is the job of the Panama Canal pilots. Most of them were licensed shipmasters before they trained for half a year to become pilots. Then for another year, as probationary pilots, they gained experience in taking all kinds of ships through the canal.

Guiding ships through this waterway needs special skill. At Panama the waters of the Atlantic and Pacific oceans wash two coasts only forty-five miles apart. Here is one of the narrowest points on Central America's long skinny neck. From Mexico to Colombia a mountain chain marches down the winding ridge of land. At the Panama Canal Zone these mountains dip to low hills, but the middle section of the zone is still quite high. Somehow the ships in the canal must climb across the high place, and only especially skilled pilots can guide them.

For about eight miles inland from the buoys that mark the Pacific entrance the Panama Canal is at sea level. Tides here sometimes change the ocean level as much as twenty feet, but the canal is built so that ships navigate safely at high or low tide.

Likewise, from the breakwater on the Atlantic side of the Panama Canal Zone ships go inland at sea level for about eight miles. The difference in tides in this ocean is only about three feet.

5

Air view of the Panama Canal

Between these two sea-level channels lie Gatun Lake, a man-made body of water on the canal, and Gaillard Cut. This whole middle part of the canal is 85 feet above sea level.

If the canal is to work, ships must be raised from the two sea-level channels to the higher level of Gatun Lake and Gaillard Cut. Then, once the ships have passed through the greater part

6

of the canal at this high level, they must be lowered again to sea level.

The raising and lowering is done by three double sets of water stairs called "locks." A lock is a high-walled chamber with a gate at each end, built into a canal. It works like this.

As a ship that is to be raised approaches the lock, the entrance gate opens. At this time the water in the lock is at the same level as the water outside, where the ship is floating.

The ship enters easily, but once inside the lock the gate closes. Now water pours into the lock through openings in its walls or floor. As the water level rises, the ship rises also.

Slowly it goes up, until it is on a level with the higher part of the canal. Then the water stops rising, and the exit gate of the lock is opened. The ship floats easily out of the lock chamber and goes on its way.

If a ship is to be lowered, the lock works in the opposite way. The vessel enters a lock full of water. But once it is inside, the water runs out of the chamber until the ship is brought down to the lower canal level.

In the Panama Canal two water steps are placed together at Miraflores Locks near the Pacific end of the canal. These locks

7

raise ships 54 feet above sea level. Then the ships pass through small Miraflores Lake. They go up the final step at Pedro Miguel Locks. Now they are 85 feet above sea level. To go down again on the Atlantic end, they pass through three chambers, or stairs, all built together at Gatun Locks.

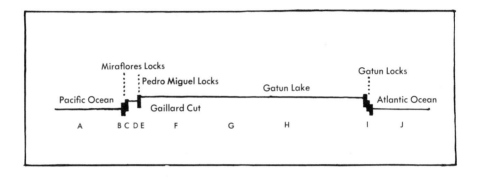

PROFILE OF THE PANAMA CANAL

A. A ship approaches at sea level.

B. At Miraflores Locks the first chamber raises the vessel 27 feet.

C. The second chamber raises it up the water stairs another 27 feet.

D. Now, 54 feet above sea level, the ship proceeds 1½ miles through Miraflores Lake.

E. Pedro Miguel Locks' single flight raises the ship 31 feet. Now the ship has come 85 feet above sea level. She will remain at this height for most of her passage through the canal.

F. The ship moves through Gaillard Cut.

G. At the town of Gamboa the Chagres River enters the canal.

H. Now the canal widens into Gatun Lake.

I. At Gatun Locks the ship goes "down the stairs" to sea level again. In three steps, about 28 feet at a time, the ship moves from lock chamber to lock chamber.

J. At sea level once more, the ship goes through the eight-mile channel that takes her out to the Atlantic Ocean.

No pumps are used to fill or empty the canal's lock chambers. The water simply runs downhill from Gatun Lake, which is ringed in by the solid banks of Gatun Dam, 85 feet above sea level. The lake level is higher than that of any of the locks before they are filled, so that the water runs into the locks easily. It flows from one level to another through large tunnels located in the center and side walls of the locks. From these tunnels the water flows through smaller culverts opening into the walls and floors of the lock chambers.

To lift a ship up one single water step, 26 million gallons of water are needed. That is as much water as the whole of a medium-sized city uses in a day! Twice as much water — 52 million gallons — is needed to take a ship all the way through the canal. But there is rarely a water shortage in the Panama Canal Zone. The Isthmus of Panama has a tremendous rainfall. The huge amount of water needed to operate the canal is stored in Gatun and Madden lakes during the long rainy season, and is used all the year through.

Now on the *Tosca* the pilot orders, "Slow speed ahead!" The chief officer pulls a lever called a "telegraph." It is marked with several speeds. He sets it at slow speed, which is marked on this control in Swedish, "*Helt sakta.*" By moving the telegraph on the bridge the officer signals the engine room far below in the ship. There the order will be carried out.

At the ship's log book next to the telegraph another officer writes, "6 A. M. Slow speed." Each order that the pilot gives during the trip through the canal will be recorded in the ship's log.

The sleek freighter moves easily into the channel. The long fingers of Balboa Harbor's piers reach out into the water at the right. Farther ahead, at the left, lie the trim gray piers of the

9

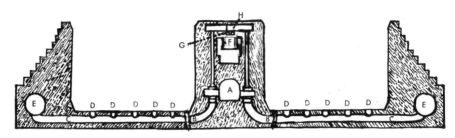

Cross section of lock chambers and walls, Gatun Locks

HOW A PANAMA CANAL LOCK IS BUILT

A. Water pours through this huge culvert in the center wall of the lock. The pipe is so large that a locomotive could go through it.

B. Smaller culverts like this one run from A under the lock floor.

C. Lateral culverts also come off large culvert E in the side wall of the lock.

D. These wells, which run all along the lock floor, open into the culverts beneath them. When the wells are all open, water pours in or out of them quickly. In eight minutes 26 million gallons of water can pour in or out of the lock chamber.

E. The large culvert running through the side lock wall.

F. The drainage gallery in the center lock wall.

G. Electrical wiring runs through the lock wall. It carries current to operate gate and valve machinery.

H. A passageway is built inside the center lock wall for the lock operators.

To fill a lock the valves at the upper end are opened and the valves at the lower end are closed. The water flows from the upper pool through the large culverts into the small lateral culverts and from there through the holes in the floor into the lock chamber. To empty a lock the valves at the upper end are closed and those at the lower end are opened, and the water flows into the lower lock or pool.

10

United States naval base. Soon the pilot orders the ship to slow down for a launch that is coming alongside. Up the ladder file the men of the line-handling crew. They will secure towing cables to the ship when she reaches the locks.

The pilot stands alert. He has never been on the *Tosca* before, and in these first few minutes he is getting her feel. He asks the chief officer how well she handles at very slow speeds, and how many knots (nautical miles per hour) she goes at "dead slow." Each ship behaves a little differently from any other. Before the pilot comes to the tricky passage through the locks he must know all he can about handling the *Tosca*. Many new ships are geared to high speeds. Keeping them down to the canal's speed limit for safety is a real problem for the pilot. Oftentimes a ship does not steer well when she is going very slowly.

The harbor has narrowed down to a 500-foot channel. The ship has gone over six miles when up ahead loom the tall black gates and the white tower of Miraflores Locks.

"Stop!" orders Captain Nilsen.

"Stop!" echoes the quartermaster.

The *Tosca* slows down as her engines are stopped. Now the long concrete walls of Miraflores Locks overshadow her. A little rowboat comes alongside. It carries rope lines from the mechanical "mules" — the famous Panama Canal towing locomotives. One hundred years ago real mules towed ships through smaller canals, and the locomotives are often called "mules" even today.

The line-handlers on the deck of the *Tosca* throw down to the rowboat one end of a slender manila line called a "messenger." The man in the rowboat ties the messenger to the line from one of the towing locomotives. This is tied in turn to the

11

Locomotives, often called "mules," tow ships through the locks

steel-wire towing cable from the mule. The deck crew now pulls up on the messenger line and on the heavier line, or hawser, until the end of the steel cable from the locomotive is pulled up onto the ship. There the eye of the cable is thrown over a "bitt" — a steel fastening point on the deck of the ship — and the cable is made fast.

The *Tosca* is a medium-sized freighter. She is a "six-locomotive lockage" — that is, six locomotives are needed to take her through the locks, three locomotives on each side. The two front mules do the actual pulling. The middle two help control the ship by pulling or braking as the pilot commands. The last two act only as brakes.

At last the steel cable from each mule is made fast. Now the big black lock gates, each one weighing seven hundred tons,

swing silently open. These gates are made of steel seven feet thick. They are not solid, though. Instead, they have hollow, watertight compartments. They almost float as they move open and fit snugly into the walls of the lock. Beyond them the lock chamber appears. It comes almost as a surprise that the water level of the chamber ahead is at exactly the same level as the part of the canal where the *Tosca* floats.

The pilot leans out through the open windows of the bridge. Each of the locomotive operators is looking up at him for a signal. He raises both arms over his head. Then he lowers them to shoulder level. His signal means, "Begin towing!"

The cables go taut as the two front locomotives move ahead. The ship's engines help, too, and take some of the strain from the mules. The pilot hurries over to the side of the ship. He looks down to see how close the *Tosca* is moving to the concrete walls. He calls back new orders to the quartermaster.

Water movements and wind join to jar the ship out of its careful place in the middle of the chamber. The pilot must watch these things. He must give the proper orders to keep the ship standing clear of the walls.

The gates close behind the *Tosca*. Now she is shut up in the thousand-foot-long lock chamber, ready to "start upstairs" on the Panama Canal's "staircase over the mountains."

Up in the locks control tower the operator has been watching the *Tosca*. He moved the switch that opened and closed the lock gates. Now he throws the switch that opens huge valves in the lock floor and center wall. As if a stopper had been pulled

13

from a bathtub, the water rushes out of the chamber ahead of the *Tosca*. It pours through culverts into the chamber where the ship now floats. Twenty-six million gallons of water enter the chamber in eight minutes. It comes in so smoothly that hardly a bubble shows on the surface. As the chamber fills with water, the ship rises. In eight minutes she comes up 27 feet. Now she is ready to go up a second step.

The lock gates open in front of her. There lies the second chamber, at exactly the water level the *Tosca* has risen to. The pilot gives the arm signal again. The towing locomotives answer the signal with a "Ding! Ding!" With the mules leading the way, the ship moves into the next chamber. When the lock gates are safely closed, the control operator moves another switch. Another 26 million gallons of water raise the *Tosca* 27 feet in eight more minutes. She is sitting 54 feet above the level of the Pacific Ocean.

Now the *Tosca* is ready to go out of the locks. The gates open. The locomotives tow the ship through. Then the pilot crosses his arms and swings them outward. "Stop towing!" the signal says to the mule operators. The tow lines fall away from the ship. The pilot presses a button that blows the ship's whistle.

"Clear of the locks!" the whistle means. As if happy to escape this closed-in space, the ship spurts out into the channel.

When the *Tosca* has gone about a mile, the pilot orders, "Stop the engines!" The ship has come to Pedro Miguel Locks. There is only one step here. Just as at Miraflores Locks, the ship rises — this time 31 feet. Now the *Tosca* sits 85 feet above sea level. She will travel at this height for almost all the rest of the way across the Canal Zone. Just before reaching the Atlantic Ocean, she will go downstairs — one, two, three, to sea level — in Gatun Lock's three chambers.

All day long the locks are busy

Balls and a cone are signals to direct ships through the Cut

Once the ship is clear of Pedro Miguel Locks, the pilot calls out, "Dead slow!"

The *Tosca* is entering Gaillard Cut, the most treacherous stretch of the canal. Green grassy banks rise on either side of the channel. The pilot picks up his binoculars and focuses on the distant left bank of the canal. Just before a curve stands the Cucaracha Signal Station. The glasses show clearly a big black zero posted out in front of the little building. The zero means that there are no ships coming from the other direction. A mast like that of a ship rises above the signal station. From it hangs a ball, with a pointed cone above it — the signal for the *Tosca* to go ahead northward.

16

Luckily it is too early in the day for a ship to have come this far south from the Atlantic Ocean. If it were later and a ship were approaching the *Tosca,* the pilot would be faced with the tricky job of passing it in the Cut. To do this, the ships go head on toward each other. When they are a few hundred feet apart, each pilot heads the bow of his ship to starboard. As the ships pass, water currents may draw them dangerously close to each other. At the same time, currents pulling from the bank may draw the stern of the ship out of the channel toward the shore. The pilots must take care to keep their ships in the clear.

Huge ships — battleships, big passenger liners, and large ore ships and tankers — do not pass any other ship in the Cut. All traffic from the opposite direction stops while one of the giant ships goes through with a "clear Cut."

Smaller ships can meet and pass in the Cut

17

Past Cucaracha Station the hills rise higher on either side of the narrow channel. The ship is reaching the high backbone of the land. Jungle grass now covers the scarred rock banks that rise on either side of the *Tosca*. Each cubic yard of rock blasted out here took the mighty effort of hundreds of canal construction workers.

On the left the *Tosca* sails past the freshly cut, flat terraces of Contractors Hill. Here in 1955 a deep crack in the ground was found to be widening fast. It threatened to send the whole hill sliding into the water. Trucks and power shovels arrived in time to take thousands of tons of earth from the slope before it could slip to block the canal.

Now the highest point along the canal looms above the *Tosca* on the right. It is the black rock of Gold Hill, rising jagged and rough from the water. Ahead of Gold Hill the channel bends. A large "W" sign stands on the bank. It reminds the pilot to blow the whistle as the ship rounds the bend, to warn any ship that might be ahead around the blind curve.

All through the Cut markers called "ranges" are posted to guide the pilots. The markers are black crosses painted on white signboards and placed in pairs, one above the other, in the hills. The pilot steers his ship so that the lower cross of each pair appears to be lined up exactly with the one above it. By lining up the markers in this way he is sure to stay in the deep channel of the twisting Cut.

Captain Nilsen raises his binoculars and checks the distant pair of ranges. "Starboard ten . . . Midships . . . Ease to five!" he commands. Minute by minute these brief orders shift the ship a few degrees to port or starboard and keep her in mid-channel.

The pilot's quiet orders and the quartermaster's echo are the only sounds on the bridge. The officer patiently writes each order in the log. The ship's captain stands silent behind the pilot. He watches closely as this stranger who has taken command of his ship guides her in the narrow waterway.

At last the end of the dangerous Cut is in sight. The pilot relaxes a bit as the canal widens to a more comfortable five hundred feet. The town of Gamboa appears on the right bank. Just before it the Chagres River flows into the canal. The ship has passed safely through Gaillard Cut.

The pilot orders the ship to increase speed to eight knots. Now the canal widens gradually, for here, where the Chagres River enters, Gatun Lake begins. The *Tosca* is sailing into one of the world's large artificial lakes. It covers an area of almost 164 square miles, and was made by damming the Chagres River near the Atlantic Ocean. Now, instead of flowing into the sea, the water in the river has backed up and formed a huge lake. This lake supplies the water needed to operate the locks.

As Gatun Lake widens, it sprawls for miles in all directions. Buoys mark the course of the channel across the big lake — a strange, twisting course that follows the valley of the Chagres River, now lying far under water.

In Gatun Lake the *Tosca* can go as fast as fifteen knots, as the channel is a thousand feet wide here. It is past noon now. The pilot has been standing on the bridge for more than six hours. A steward appears with a lunch tray for him. Captain Nilsen does not leave his post, but while his ship moves through the thousand-foot channel he takes a few minutes to eat.

He points out the site of the town of Gorgona to the captain as the ship passes over it. Gorgona lay in the path of Gatun Lake. When the water began rising behind the dam, the town's resi-

19

Gatun Lake is large, with a wide channel

dents were moved away. Gorgona now lies buried under 80 feet
of water. Old mango trees stand on the shore of the lake. Behind
them are banana groves gone wild. These trees may have been
on the fringes of the town fifty years ago.

"Port five . . . Port ten . . . Midships."

The pilot's orders move the ship through the winding channel.
Her course takes her in and out among clumps of islands high
with jungle grass. Skeletons of trees dead for forty years stick
up through the calm water just beyond the channel markers.
Clusters of tropical orchids blister the gray trunks. These ghosts
of the past remind travelers on passing ships that thick green
jungle once grew where Gatun Lake now is.

In a few minutes the *Tosca* meets the first ship of the day,

20

coming from the Atlantic. She is a new Danish freighter, the *Halldor*. She is bound for Yokohama, Japan, from Baltimore, and carries six thousand tons of steel sheets and pig iron. The *City of Karachi*, a British freighter out of London follows, with a blue star painted on her stack. She carries tractors and tobacco to Australia. A spanking-white fruit ship of the United Fruit Company's "Great White Fleet" sails by in ballast, riding high and empty. She is going up the Pacific coast to pick up a load of bananas.

A few minutes later a dark Norwegian tanker, the *Rogn*, slithers by with tanks full of fuel oil for Ecuador. She is followed by another Norwegian, a black and white freighter, the ship *Vindegger*. She carries asbestos and newsprint from Canada to

21

There are three steps in the Gatun Locks

Colombia. All her flags and pennants are flying gaily, decorating her masts with many colors. The pilot points out that this is Norway's Constitution Day. The *Vindegger*, passing through a canal thousands of miles from Norway, lets the world see she is "dressed" for the holiday.

Gatun Lake gradually narrows down, and the end of the lake comes into sight. Its jungle-clad shores hide the huge earthworks that hold back the broad waters. On the left shore appears the broad concrete wall of Gatun Dam. Earth and concrete form the dike that keeps Gatun Lake from running down into the sea.

To the right of the wall stands the white tower that marks Gatun Locks. The *Tosca* has come to a traffic bottleneck in the canal. It is almost two o'clock in the afternoon. A few ships are only now coming up the water stairs of Gatun Locks — beginning the journey from the Atlantic to the Pacific. The pilot gives orders to drop anchor. There will be a wait before the *Tosca* can go down to sea level.

The pilot walks out on deck from the bridge. A line of ships stretches behind the *Tosca* now, strung out like a huge necklace across Gatun Lake. They have followed, all the way through the canal. No ship overtakes another one in the Panama Canal. The ships behind the *Tosca* must wait for her to be locked through.

At last the locks are clear. The pilot orders the anchor raised. Then he gives the command to go ahead. Once more the lock gates swing open, into one, two, three chambers with a drop or lift of about 28 feet each. As if giant stoppers had been pulled, the water spills out of the Gatun Locks. The *Tosca* rides down to sea level again.

As the last set of gates open and the ship passes through, the pilot crosses his arms and swings them out. Ding! Ding! The towing locomotives' cables fall away. The pilot blows the whistle, and the *Tosca* goes forward under her own power. At last she has reached the sea-level channel that will take her after a few miles to the Atlantic Ocean. The pilot gives a sigh of relief.

The last few miles of channel go by quickly. Then Captain Nilsen picks up his portable ship-to-shore radio and reports to the dispatcher's office.

"We are clear out of the locks and proceeding to the anchorage," he says. "No incidents. Good afternoon."

Soon a putt-putting alongside tells that the launch has arrived to take off the pilot. He and the captain shake hands with the silent understanding of two shipmasters. With smiles they say good-bye in English and Swedish. Captain Nilsen's day of careful work is over. The *Tosca* has reached the Atlantic Ocean safely and in good time. The pilot goes down the ladder and into the waiting, sputtering launch. As it pulls away, the captain waves down to him from high up on the bridge. Once more he is in command of his own ship.

Down come the courtesy flag and the pennants — number three and "We have a pilot aboard."

"Full speed ahead!" the captain orders.

With a mighty blast of her whistle the *Tosca*, guided safely from one ocean to another by a skillful pilot, heads for the open sea. After twelve days of clear sailing she will reach another continent. Across the high seas she goes to Amsterdam, port of the Netherlands, in Europe.

Safely through the canal, a ship heads for the open sea

From a mountain peak Balboa viewed the Pacific

The Dream of a Western Passage

It took ten years to build the Panama Canal, and the canal was finally finished in 1914. But for many years before that it had been the dream of countless men. Christopher Columbus, on his fourth voyage to the Americas in 1502, sailed up and down Panama's coast looking for the magic passage to the West. He questioned the Indians at the mouth of the Chagres River, near where the canal now enters the Atlantic. Did they know of *another* sea near here? Yes, the Indians told his interpreters, there was such a sea. If Columbus would only leave his ships and follow them overland, they would show it to him. But Columbus said no. He ordered his crew to haul up anchor. He would reach that other sea by ship! He died without finding the waterway to the Orient.

25

Just a few years later, Vasco Nuñez de Balboa journeyed overland at Panama. He found what Columbus would not leave his ships to discover. From a mountain peak in Panama's Darien Province he was the first white man to see the Pacific Ocean from the Americas.

Soon afterward the Spanish sailed all around the great pear-shaped continent of South America. And in their travels they learned the truth. The oceans came close together, but they never quite met. There was no waterway between the continents. The mountains of Central America's ridge separated the oceans solidly, even at the narrowest places. When Spain's King Charles V heard of his explorers' sad discovery, he said that a canal ought to be dug to join the oceans. Four hundred years went by before his idea was carried out.

The Spanish did build a road from ocean to ocean, though. Exploring parties were sent through Central America to find the narrowest, least hilly place between the seas. The best place for the road, they decided, was the low basin at Panama. Near the same route they found, the Panama Canal was cut centuries later.

Just a few years after Balboa set eyes on the Pacific, the Spanish finished their road. They called it *El Camino Real*, Spanish for "The Royal Road." It started at the harbor town of Porto Bello on the Atlantic. From there the cobblestone road followed old Indian trails overland. Where it reached the Pacific Ocean the Spanish built the first city of Panama.

Soon afterward the Spanish sailed to Peru. There they found the great rich cities of the Incas. As they conquered the Indians, they sent back to Panama ships loaded to the gunwales with gold and silver. Well-guarded mule trains hauled the loot by the

The Spaniards unloaded the Inca treasure on Panama's Pacific shore

Royal Road from the Pacific shore across to Porto Bello. There the precious metals were carefully put aboard ships of the royal fleet. Under full sail the heavy-laden galleons carried their priceless cargo across the Atlantic to Spain.

During the years when the Americas were being explored and colonized, there was only one way to reach the Pacific Ocean from the Atlantic by ship. That way was the long route around Cape Horn, the southernmost tip of South America. Captains and crews of whalers and China-bound clipper ships dreaded "rounding the Horn." From Panama's Atlantic coast a ship's crew could almost smell the Pacific Ocean, lying only 45 miles west, over the horizon. But to reach the Pacific they had to sail down from the tropics and around the bulge of South America. Down, down they went for days and into the Temperate Zone again. As the weather grew colder, they reached the dangerous waters off Tierra del Fuego. There the meeting currents of the Atlantic and the Pacific boiled up into sudden, terrible storms. Through the cold and fog and between the reefs the ships sailed. Once around

Many a ship was wrecked on Cape Horn

the tip of the Horn, they had to begin the long journey up South America's west coast. But some vessels never reached the west coast. Instead, they smashed into Tierra del Fuego's reefs or capsized in its storms. Many a sturdy whaling ship and graceful clipper set off around the Horn from a northern port and never was heard from again.

Learning that another ship had been lost going around the Horn, people in the north would shake their heads sadly. If there were only a short cut — a western passage between the Americas!

The discovery of gold in California in 1849 sent streams of people hurrying toward America's West. Many gold seekers journeyed across North America in covered wagons. Others, afraid of the fierce Plains Indians, took passage on ships going around the Horn. Some traveled the Panama route in the gold rush. By the hundreds they got off ships at the Chagres River in Panama. Little boats took them up that river to an old Spanish road, Las Cruces Trail. Going overland, they reached Panama City on the Pacific Ocean in two days. There they waited for other ships to take them north to California's gold fields.

In 1855, six years after the gold rush started, the first railroad across the Americas was built — at Panama. Now a traveler bound for California could get on a crowded railroad coach at the new town of Colon on the Atlantic. The wheezing, smoky train puffed across Panama on a single row of tracks. That afternoon, whistle blowing and bell ringing, it pulled into Panama City. Ocean to ocean in four hours! A western passage by railroad was now possible!

Beginning with the gold rush, more and more settlers moved to the western part of the United States. Cities sprang up.

Ranches and farms crisscrossed land that not long before had been Indian territory. Railroads were built, and carried machinery and steel, cloth and plows to the West. And the railroads brought back to the East beef and hides, wheat and ores.

But freight moves more cheaply by ship than by railroad. And some things, too big for railroad cars, still had to be carried around the Horn by ship. Many people in the United States talked of the need for a canal through Central America. Cheap trade between the east and west coasts of the United States would be a great help to the growth of the country and its commerce.

Other countries were interested in a canal, too. Every nation that owned a large merchant fleet talked of digging a canal between the Americas. What a saving of time and money it would mean to world trade!

Then, in 1869, the Suez Canal was cut between Africa and the Near East. Now ships would not have to go around Africa to get to Asia. Days of sailing time were saved as ships poured through the water ditch at Suez. Why couldn't the same thing be done in the Americas? Writers and political leaders demanded a canal to save the long journey around South America.

In 1880 a French company decided to dig a canal between the Atlantic and Pacific oceans. It was to be at Panama. The very man who had built the Suez Canal would head the job: Count Ferdinand de Lesseps. He sailed to Panama to begin his second canal.

De Lesseps and his workers soon found that the job at Panama was much harder than at Suez. There a wide ditch had been cut through flat desert sands. Panama had mountains. It had the wild, flooding waters of the Chagres River. Its Pacific Ocean had a twenty-foot tide while the Atlantic Ocean had a tide of only about three feet.

30

Worse than all this, Panama's low swampland was one of the most unhealthful spots in the world. Yellow fever and malaria soon killed French workers by the hundreds.

De Lesseps' engineers worked on plan after plan for a canal that could go through the mountains, across a flooding river, and into two different tides. While they drew diagrams, their shovels and railroad engines rusted in the damp tropical weather.

Nine years after starting, the French gave up and fled the horrors of Panama. Their company had run out of money. They left behind some shallow ditches, deserted hospitals, and several cemeteries where thousands of workers lay buried. De Lesseps was broken-hearted. He died a few years later, forgetting his

The French left the ruins of their canal

Colonel William Crawford Gorgas

victory at Suez in his defeat at Panama. The French formed a new company and worked half-heartedly at the canal for some years. Then they left it forever.

In 1898 the Spanish-American War began. Orders went out to the United States fleet to meet at once in the Atlantic. The battleship *Oregon* was cruising in the Pacific Ocean off California, guarding the western coast, when she received the message.

Starting from San Francisco, the *Oregon* went full speed ahead down around South America. Rounding the Horn, she steamed up the long east coast. It took the *Oregon* 69 days to join the United States fleet in the Caribbean Sea. Now as never before people in the United States realized how much a canal through Central America was needed. With coasts on two oceans to defend, the fleet should have a short way to go from the Atlantic to the Pacific.

Many people thought that a canal should be dug at Nicaragua. True, there was an active volcano there. If it erupted, flowing lava could close the canal. But if the French under the great de Lesseps had failed, could the United States dig a canal at Panama?

In 1903 Panama, then a province of the republic of Colombia, revolted and declared its independence. The United States recognized the government of the new country. Earlier the United States and Colombia had not been able to agree about building a canal through Panama. But the new republic and the United

32

States government signed a treaty a few weeks after the revolution. The United States guaranteed the little country's independence. Panama in turn granted to the United States the use, occupation, and control of a strip of land ten miles wide through their country. It was granted "in perpetuity," which means forever.

This strip of land was named the Panama Canal Zone. It was to be used for building a canal, keeping it in working order, and protecting it. But could the job be done? Many intelligent people said no. With mountains, tides, rivers, fevers — building a canal was impossible, they declared.

One of the first Americans to arrive in the Canal Zone was a friendly, energetic doctor, Colonel William Crawford Gorgas of the United States Army Medical Corps. Colonel Gorgas had just come from Cuba. There he had helped clean up the city of Havana after the Spanish-American War. He had been in Cuba two years before when Colonel Walter Reed had discovered that a mosquito causes yellow fever. What a difference that discovery was to make in Panama!

Gorgas' job was to make Panama a healthful place to live in. Carefully he explored the new zone. Then he wrote to the United States government for the supplies he needed. He wanted to keep out mosquitoes by screening every door and window in the Canal Zone. The germs of cholera and other fevers were breeding in the filthy open sewers of Panama City and Colon; he asked for pipes to build modern sewers. He had to have equipment to pipe a pure water supply — and oil to spread on every stagnant pool of water where mosquitoes were breeding.

Colonel Gorgas waited for months, but his oil and screening and pipes did not come. Malaria and yellow fever began to kill

33

the canal workers. The same hospital buildings where so many of the French had died were opened for the Americans. More and more men died, but only a few hundred yards of screening arrived.

Meantime, in Washington, men were laughing at Gorgas' tremendous supply order. One official said, "Screening all the windows? He must want to turn the Isthmus of Panama into a summer resort!" He did not understand that protection by a screen could save a man's life when yellow fever and malaria mosquitoes were flying.

President Theodore Roosevelt heard about Colonel Gorgas' problem. He made sure that Gorgas got his screening. The oil and sewer and water pipes arrived in the Zone, too. Workers' homes were screened. No one was allowed to go outside at night when the mosquitoes were biting. New sewers were built. Pure water was piped through the Zone and into Colon and Panama City.

Very soon fewer people were becoming ill. On November 11, 1905, as an American worker lay dying of yellow fever in Ancon Hospital, Colonel Gorgas stood by with his fellow doctors. "Look carefully, men," he said. "This is the last case of yellow fever you will ever see."

He was right. There has never been another case of yellow fever in the Canal Zone. Cholera and smallpox disappeared and there was much less malaria. The Canal Zone became one of the most healthful tropical spots in the world.

While Gorgas was making Panama a safe place to live in, engineers were planning the canal. Many questions had to be decided quickly. How wide should the canal be? Engineers knew that a sea-level canal from ocean to ocean would be best.

Building the locks

But it would take too long to dig. How many locks should there be, then? How high must ships be raised to carry them over the hills? Could the Chagres River, with its floods and fury, be dammed up to make an artificial lake?

Many engineers came to the Canal Zone to help in the big job, but none of them stayed. At last, in 1907, President Roosevelt named Colonel George W. Goethals of the Army Engineers to head the task.

"An army man," the President said, "will go where he is sent, and he will *have* to stay. The canal *must* be dug!"

Colonel Goethals stayed. President Roosevelt made it clear that Goethals was the boss. He was in charge of the thousands of construction workers who were digging the canal. The Colonel was ready to work as hard as any of his men. He was willing to hear their complaints, too. Every Sunday morning at ten o'clock

35

Digging the Cut

he held a meeting at his home. Any worker with a problem could come to see him. Many an unhappy person took his worries to the Colonel. And dozens of workers stayed on the job because of the Colonel's help in his Sunday-morning chats.

But even the Colonel was discouraged by the landslides. Work-

36

ers would dig away for weeks into the side of Gold Hill or Contractors Hill. After dynamite had been placed and had blown the face of the rock into pieces, clumsy steam shovels would trundle in to eat away at the broken boulders. Just when a good-sized ditch had been dug, a landslide would begin. A sudden rain might start it, or a loud noise, or perhaps nothing that anyone could see or hear. With a loud crash, part of the hill would slide into the new ditch like a terrible waterfall. The heavy fall of earth would bury men in their steam shovels.

Workers were killed; weeks of work were spent in vain. With more dynamite and other steam shovels the crews would begin again.

It took ten years to do the job. At last, in 1914, the canal was finished. Bright new concrete walls marked three sets of locks — two on the Pacific end of the canal and one on the Atlantic. A huge dam now plugged the mouth of the wild Chagres River. Behind it rose one of the world's large artificial lakes, covering many square miles of jungle.

Now the canal was ready. What ship should be first to go through it? The freight passenger ship *Ancon* was chosen for the honor. This vessel had brought hundreds of workers to their jobs in the Canal Zone. Early on the morning of August 15, 1914, the *Ancon* started from the Atlantic Ocean into the newly cut channel. A few hundred lucky construction workers crowded aboard her for the historic trip. Other hundreds on the Atlantic shore waved to the *Ancon* as she steamed up the channel. Whistles and bands hailed her. At Gatun Locks the shiny new towing locomotives came to meet the ship. The lock gates opened for the first time. Crowds cheered as the ship moved into the lock chamber. The gates swung closed. They worked fine!

The signal was given to fill the lock chamber. Water rushed in; the chamber filled; and the ship rose 28 feet. The gates opened and the ship moved into the second chamber. Up she went — and out! Again she repeated her rise. The "staircase over the mountains" was a success!

On through the canal the ship sailed. All along the route people watched her progress. Late that afternoon she entered the Pacific Ocean in triumph. Whistles blew. Flags waved. Crowds cheered. The *Ancon* had gone from the Atlantic to the Pacific in eight and one half hours.

Building the Panama Canal had taken many years, many millions of dollars, and many lives. But Columbus' dream of a western passage had come true. At last the land had been cut and the oceans joined.

Gatun Locks

38

Major General George Washington Goethals

Keeping the Canal Running

Now that the great job of building the Panama Canal was finished, General Goethals was given a special honor. The President of the United States appointed him as first governor of the Panama Canal Zone. Since then each governor has been appointed from General Goethals' outfit, the Corps of Army Engineers, for a four-year term.

The job of running the waterway belongs to the marine director. He is always an officer of the United States Navy, and is chosen for a three-year term.

In addition, many specialists are needed to keep the canal working. Nearly 3,500 United States citizens live in the Canal Zone and work for the Panama Canal agencies of the United States government. These citizens belong to seven hundred professions and trades. Pilots, dredging engineers, lockmasters, lawyers, teachers, tugboat operators, doctors, policemen, mechanics, and shipfitters are only a few of them. Dozens of canal employees or their wives are children or grandchildren of men who came to work under General Goethals when the canal was being built.

Citizens of Panama have an equal chance with United States citizens for positions. Nearly ten thousand Panamanians work for the Panama Canal agencies.

39

At each end of the canal is a port for vessels

Running this waterway for the world is expensive. In addition to the day-to-day work of getting the ships through, there is the cost of repairs and upkeep. Three sets of locks must be kept working smoothly; every five years they must be overhauled. A large force of pilots must be trained to take ships through. The channel must be dredged constantly to keep it always 42 feet deep. At Balboa on the Pacific coast, and Cristobal on the Atlantic, ports must be kept open to vessels twenty-four hours a day. And there is also the expense of keeping the Canal Zone the healthful place that Colonel Gorgas made it.

The ships that go through the Panama Canal from all over the world pay tolls to keep the waterway running. An average-sized freight ship pays $4,000 to go through the canal. It would cost the same ship about $50,000 and twenty precious days of sailing time to go around South America.

Toll rates are figured by the ton. Ships carrying cargo pay 90¢ a ton. Ships in ballast — freight ships without cargo — pay 72¢ a ton. Ships of the world's navies, passenger ships, and other ships that carry no cargo pay 50¢ a ton. United States ships pay the same rates as do those of any other nation.

The Panama Canal Company is the United States government body that keeps the canal running. Out of the money received

The Canal Zone has been made into a healthful place

41

from tolls, it pays $1,930,000 each year to the Republic of Panama under the treaty agreements.

The United States government provides money each year for employees' housing, schools, hospitals, police protection, and other community services. This money is paid back to the government out of money the Canal Company receives in tolls.

The Panama Canal pays its own way. The United States taxpayers do not spend a cent to keep it running. The United States, on the other hand, does not try to make a profit from the canal.

The cost of military protection for the canal is taken care of by the Department of Defense. It is very, very important that this busy waterway be carefully guarded. The United States Army, Navy, and Air Force all have bases in the Canal Zone; and the country's defense of the Caribbean Sea is centered in the Zone at the headquarters of the Caribbean Command.

Who Uses the Canal?

Big passenger ships carrying tourists on long cruises are exciting to watch as they pass through the canal. But they are beautiful rare birds that pass through chiefly during the winter months of the tourist season. The freight-passenger ships that run on regular schedules use the canal much more often. American ships run regularly to South America. Italian and German ships carry passengers through to Europe from western North and South America.

Passenger ships journey back and forth from New Zealand to England through the Panama Canal. The canal route is the shortest one between New Zealand and her mother country. Since World War II thousands of European people have gone through the canal, bound for new homes in New Zealand and Australia.

43

Ships of commerce are the canal's chief users

But since World War II the passenger traffic is only half of what it used to be. Many people in a hurry now travel across the oceans by air. That does not mean that the canal is used less, however. It is busier than ever before. People are journeying all over the world now, carrying new ideas and new ways of living to undeveloped lands. And the materials to build up backward countries go by ship. Road-building machinery, dredges to make new ports, steel for new buildings, derricks to pump untapped oil, rails for new railroads, all travel by ship. Much of that cargo goes through the Panama Canal.

The freight ships of the world are the canal's chief users. They funnel through the waterway from 72 different trade routes. The money they save by using this short cut amounts to 150 million dollars a year.

More than half the ships that use the canal are going to or coming from the United States. Important in this traffic are the American ships that sail regularly between the east and west coasts of that country.

Ships that pass through the canal with cargoes bound for the United States carry raw materials mostly. Ores, fuel, and other materials are needed to feed the busy American factories. And some things must be brought in from outside because the United States does not have them at all. Manila fiber for making rope comes through the canal from the Philippines. Rubber comes through the canal short cut from Indonesia and Thailand; coffee from Colombia, Chile, and Peru; tin from Chile and Peru.

Tremendous ore ships carry iron ore regularly from Peru to Philadelphia and Baltimore. The eastern United States needs lumber, too. Ships from the Pacific Northwest and Canada move

45

through the canal, their decks piled high with lumber.

The United States uses the canal more than any other country. Ships registered in England, Norway, Germany, Japan, Panama, and Liberia are the next most frequent users; but many other countries are grateful for the Panama Canal, too.

Italian, British, Norwegian, and German ships run up and down South America's west coast frequently. They carry machinery and other manufactured goods from Europe to Chile and Peru. They pick up ores, coal, and fertilizers to take back to their home ports. Japanese ships go through the canal almost every day. They take manufactured goods to the east coast of the United States and South America. Then back to Japan they hurry with the coal, pig iron, and steel bars that country lacks.

The magic passageway between the oceans has helped to build up countries far from the canal. Chile, for instance, depends on the Panama Canal as if it were a lifeline. Soon after the waterway opened, nitrate mining became a thriving industry in Chile. Loaded on ships, this mineral for fertilizer went through the canal to the eastern United States and to Europe. Now nitrates are less important because artificial fertilizers can be made, but today Chile trades other cargoes as well. Out of the country's rich earth thousands of tons of valuable copper, tin, and nickel are mined each year. These minerals travel to the United States, England, Italy, and Germany by way of the Panama Canal.

Everything from hairpins to huge steel derricks appears on the cargo lists that ships must present before they enter the canal. By watching the cargoes, a person can trace what is going on all over the world. Trouble in the Near East cut off its huge oil output in 1955. A few weeks later many strange black tankers flying the red explosives flag were steaming through the canal.

Oil to turn the wheels of the world was being carried over a different route.

When the Suez Canal closed for several months in 1957, dozens of strange ships appeared for the first time at Panama. Australian, Free Chinese, and Russian ships — all used to running regularly through Suez — arrived. Some of these ships were like an embarrassed boy at a new school; they were newcomers who didn't know the rules. They all had to be admeasured, since there was no record of their measurements in the Panama Canal files. They had to choose ship's agents to arrange for tolls payment. Many of them did not own a United States flag; they had to send quickly for courtesy flags to fly while going through the waterway.

Headlines in today's papers will be felt in the Panama Canal traffic a month from now. What ships are using the canal? What cargoes are they carrying? Where are they taking their loads? The answers to these questions can change from day to day. The fruit crop fails in Italy and Spain, and ships file through the waterway with extra banana shipments for Europe. A famine strikes in South Korea, and ships carrying wheat to starving people hurry through the short cut. Canada completes a big aluminum- processing plant in British Columbia, and a new trade route is traced on the oceans to carry bauxite ore from Jamaica through the canal to the plant in western Canada.

A freight ship blasts its tremendous whistle as it steams into the Panama Canal. Somewhere, perhaps halfway around the world, something has happened in business or politics to send that ship cruising through the winding waterway. Weather, a revolution, crop failure, a business boom or a depression — all can be marked and charted by the changing line of traffic through the Panama Canal.

Today larger ships are being built than ever before

The Canal of the Future

The concrete lock walls in the Panama Canal stand only 110 feet apart. Those 110 feet are beginning to raise a great problem in the future of the waterway.

When the locks were built, Goethals and his fellow engineers did not dream of today's huge ships, which only modern ship engines have made possible. And the canal's engineers faced a problem. Would lock gates wider than 110 feet be strong enough to stand up to the strain of constant opening and closing? It

48

A U. S. battleship scrapes through a lock

was thought wisest not to chance too great a width.

For many years, as stronger engines made it possible to build larger vessels, ship designers carefully remembered the measurements of the Panama Canal locks. "One hundred and ten feet by one thousand," they said to themselves as they drew plans for new ships.

When the *Queen Mary* was launched in 1936, here was a ship 118.5 feet wide. She was 8.5 feet too broad in the beam ever to pass through the concrete locks of the Panama Canal. But that fact was not important. She and her sister ship the *Queen Elizabeth,* which was launched a little later, were designed especially for transatlantic service. They would not need to use the canal.

During World War II the United States Navy launched giant aircraft carriers and enormous battleships. In building all of them, designers remembered the lock measurements of the Panama Canal. No ship must be too wide to pass through that waterway.

All the battleships of the United States fleet can go through the Panama Canal, although they need the help of five pilots to do it. One pilot stands on the bridge and four others are spaced around the ship. They give orders by portable radio as the battleship moves through the locks with only inches to spare. The screeching and scraping can be heard for a mile away as a towering gray monster like the 108-foot-wide *Missouri* is tugged through by ten straining locomotives. Paint has been scraped off the hulls of battleships. The wooden fenders that protect the concrete walls have been splintered. But no big damage has ever been suffered by these giants of the fleet as they passed through the canal.

With the flight decks of the United States Navy's aircraft carriers carefully built to be just under 110 feet, many carriers have been squeezed through the locks. The first big one to pass

A plane carrier in the Cut

through lopped off a lamp post that hung out over the lock tower at Gatun. After that the outstretched necks of the lights were turned around, and the overhanging roofs of the lock towers were put on hinges. Now they could protect the tower crew from sun and rain on most days. But when a carrier came through, the roof could be raised out of the broad sweep of the flight deck.

After World War II, when jet planes came into use, it was found that they could land more safely on a flight deck at an angle. The angled landing made the flight deck wider than 110 feet — too wide to pass through the canal. In respect to aircraft carriers the United States now has a two-ocean navy. It takes a

month for one of the ships to go around the Horn, from one
ocean to another.

Now several large oil tankers have been built. The canal's
42-foot channel is too shallow for them, and some of them are
too long for the thousand-foot-long locks. So far, the big tankers
are traveling on routes that do not go near the Panama Canal.
But the day may come when tankers that need to pass through
the waterway will not fit.

Freight ships are growing in size, too. Panama Canal engineers
are beginning to worry. They can see that some day the canal
may be too narrow for the trade that uses it most.

Many new ships that will fit the locks are too big to pass
another ship in Gaillard Cut. Traffic through the canal is sharply

The traffic control room

slowed down when Gaillard Cut becomes a "one-way street." Sometimes, while one ship has a "clear Cut," fifteen or eighteen others must wait in Miraflores Lake or Gatun Lake.

When three or four "clear Cut" ships arrive in one day, the marine traffic control staff has a real problem. They look at their control board as if it were a tight game of chess. What ship should move first in order to save the most time for every vessel? Every ship goes through the canal so that it may save time. Time is money on the high seas, for a crew must be paid, and perishable cargo moved.

Gaillard Cut will soon be widened and dredged to five hundred feet. That has been done already for a short way. But the concrete locks cannot be stretched an inch. The problem of the future is: how can the Panama Canal be enlarged?

The United States Congress took some first steps toward enlarging the canal in 1939. The plan was to build a third set of locks alongside the present ones. Work was started, but stopped after the United States entered World War II. At that time it was important that everyone work to help the war effort.

Congress studied the problem of the canal again in 1947. The effects of bombing during the war had raised a new question. Since one good-sized bomb could destroy the locks, should a lock canal be built at all? Many people felt that the best way to improve the canal would be to dig a new one from ocean to ocean *at sea level*. Then there would be no locks, no dam, and no artificial lake to be protected from air attack.

The sea-level canal plan is for a broad, open waterway free of dangerous curves, and six hundred feet wide. It would be about five miles shorter than the present canal. Ships could pass

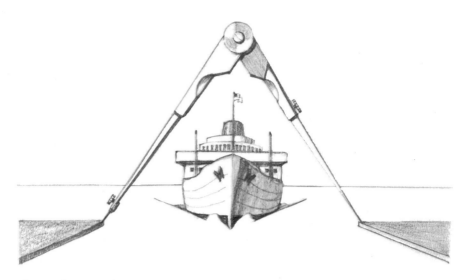

through it in half the time they take today, and even big ships could pass each other in its channel.

But what about the big difference in the tides of the two oceans? With a twenty-foot Pacific tide and a three-foot Atlantic tide, would the canal between them stir up dangerous water currents? It has been decided that ships could navigate in spite of the currents. But a tidal lock would make their passage safer. The lock would operate only when the tidal currents ran high. Except for the tidal lock, there would be clear sailing from ocean to ocean.

A sea-level canal would cost over three billion dollars, and would take ten years to dig. Traffic on the present canal would not be closed during that time except for seven days at the very end. In that last week, land plugs would be removed from the channel near each ocean, and Gatun Lake would run out into the sea.

Some other engineers favor another plan for the canal. This

calls for a new set of larger three-chamber locks at Gatun and a three-step set at Miraflores. Pedro Miguel Locks would not be rebuilt. The lake behind Miraflores Locks would be raised to the same level as Gatun Lake.

Deciding how to make the canal bigger and when to do it is the problem of the United States Congress. Pilots continue to put ships carefully through the waterway. Accidents are bound to happen now and then as bigger ships geared to higher speeds move through the narrow locks and dangerous channel. Every few months a ship runs aground or scrapes a lock wall.

Yet the Panama Canal of today stands as a modern miracle of engineering genius. Without any major changes it has worked well since 1914. The trade of the world moves through it; and the commerce of the United States depends on it. Peoples have been brought closer together by it; and it has helped make a better life for millions who live along the 72 trade routes it serves. The oceans have been joined, and a passageway made through the Americas.

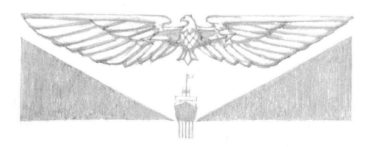

All Kinds of Ships Go

Since the *Ancon* passed through the canal on August 15, 1914, all manner of ships have gone from ocean to ocean through this waterway. The largest was the United States battleship *Missouri*, which weighed 45,000 tons.

Whaling fleets of several ships, large and small, have gone through the canal.

Probably the strangest-looking craft to go through the canal were the floating dry docks. These huge steel structures were used in the Pacific during World War II. They were too wide to go through the locks, so tanks were fastened to one side of them. As these tanks were filled with water, the side of the dock to which they were attached sank. The other side rose high in the air. Sideways the docks were hauled through the canal.

Through The Canal

Sometimes a ship comes to the canal and the owners cannot afford to pay the toll charges. Such a tramp steamer sits forlornly outside the canal entrance, sometimes for weeks. Finally the money to pay the canal treasurer arrives. The tolls are paid, and the ship goes proudly on its way through the canal.

The smallest boats to go through the canal are little hand-hollowed canoes called "cayucos," made by Panama's Indians. Canal Zone Boy Scouts in teams paddle these tiny craft from the Atlantic to the Pacific in a three-day race each year.

A forlorn-looking, boarded-up ferry boat went through the canal some years ago. The bridge across San Francisco Bay was completed, and the harbor ferry boat was no longer needed. Under its own power it rumbled through the canal, bound for Argentina. There it has a job again, carrying passengers from Buenos Aires to Montevideo in Uruguay.

57

Panama Canal Facts and Figures

Distances

	Miles
Airline distance between Balboa on Pacific and Cristobal on Atlantic	36
Length of canal, deep water to deep water	50
Shoreline distance of Gatun Lake	1,100
Distance saved by ships, New York to San Francisco	7,873

Dimensions

	Feet
Length of each lock chamber	1,000
Width of each lock chamber	110
Depth of each lock chamber	70
Minimum depth of water in each lock	40
Width of each lock gate leaf	65
Height of lock gates	47-82
Thickness of each lock gate leaf	7
Diameter of main culverts to fill locks	18

Numbers

Towing locomotives	70
Towing locomotives used for each ship	4 to 10
Daily average total passages (for 1957)	27.77
Total ocean-going commercial passages in 1957	8,579
Total canal passages of all vessels to July 1, 1957	263,934
Tons of cargo shipped through the canal to Dec. 12, 1956	One billion tons

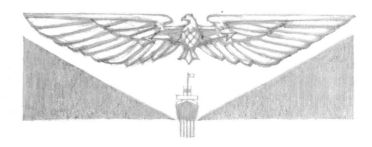

Other Books To Read

Considine, R. B.   *The Panama Canal*   Random House   1951

Fast, H. M.   *Goethals and the Panama Canal*   Messner   1942

Judson, C. I.   *Soldier Doctor; the Story of William Gorgas*
  Scribner   1942

Wood, L. N.   *Walter Reed, Doctor in Uniform*   Messner   1943

Index